· THE ·
CASEBOOKS OF
SHERLOCK HOLMES

Featuring four mysteries to solve:

The Pound of the Baskervilles

The Forger and the Fake

The Poisoned Apprentice

The Adventure of the Found Finger

221b Baker Street

Marylebone

London

NW1

Dear Reader,

I am writing to you in the now slightly more familiar position of requiring your assistance. Once again, Dr Watson has been called away on a medical assignment and my cases are threatening to spill out of my door and swamp all of Baker Street. After your most excellent help on my last four adventures, I know you are more than up to the task.

As word of my success and news that I have the help of a talented new assistant (you) has spread, more and more pitiful persons arrive at my door looking for me to help them understand the misdeeds that have been done unto them: murders and forgeries and even locating the owner of the occasional missing limb. One thing is for certain - the work of a professional detective is as varied as it is relentless. Without your help, there are frankly too many crimes for me to investigate alone.

In this book, you will find four new and exciting mysteries that I have thus been unable to crack. I have collected all of the clues

I thought may be of use: statements from witnesses, photographs, sketches and diary entries, and arranged them alongside my notes. Your task is to untangle the tales told on each page to solve each of the crimes.

Once again, I am asking you to pit your wits against some of the most cunning criminals of our age. There will be danger and thus I implore you to proceed with the utmost care. The most monstrous of crimes are committed to ensure hellish deeds remain hidden.

I have faith that with your extraordinary powers of observation and my own immense faculties, we will find solutions and peace for the distressed individuals who seek my aid. So, dear reader, will you afford me your Watsonian abilities?
The answer is surely elementary.

Yours faithfully,

Sherlock Holmes

The Pound of the Baskervilles

This case, brought to me by a Mrs Susannah Tuft, sees my return to a place I never thought I would visit again: Grimpen in Devonshire and the grounds of Baskerville Hall. Susannah had travelled down to her aunt's house in Grimpen to enter her much-admired Dalmatian into the annual Pattock's Show, held on the Baskerville estate. I thought this rather an odd pairing. A house with a reputation for being the territory of a monstrous demonic hound serving as host to a good-spirited dog competition, but I have seen stranger things than this in my long career, so I shall let it pass for now.

Susannah, it must be said, was very distressed. Beside her sat a very handsome if a little smudged Dalmatian.

She showed me this page from a book, featuring her dog, Pebbles.

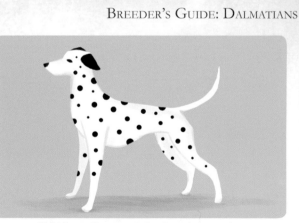

BREEDER'S GUIDE: DALMATIANS

Pebbles, a fine example of perfect spotting

The Dalmatian is a strong, muscular yet elegant dog with a symmetrical outline. Dalmatians are typically friendly and outgoing, and are rarely nervous or aggressive in nature. The ideal Dalmatian colouring is a pure white ground with dense black or liver brown spots. Tricolouring is not desirable in competition.

Mr Holmes, I am so glad you were home. I took the overnight train up from Devon and came straight here. The most terrible thing has happened at the Pattock's Dog Show. The most villainous case of dognapping!

This, Mr Holmes, is an imposter! (Indicating the dog at her side.)

The day had started so well. Pebbles was freshly bathed and groomed and was his usual sprightly self. Shy Dalmatians are marked down, did you know? But Pebbles has always been very friendly.

This dog is shy. This dog is NOT a show dog. This dog is not Pebbles. See his nose? What colour would you call that? Pink and black is what that is. Pebbles had a black nose. Prize-winning Dalmatians must have all-black noses.

Sometime after the show someone must have stolen my dear Pebbles and then dyed, inked or boot polished-up this inferior hound to look like Pebbles. How could anyone do such a thing? I ask you, Mr Holmes. Have you ever heard of a crime so dreadful?

I didn't notice right away because of all the excitement, but I later observed that my dress and hands were covered in something black that was hard to wipe off. That's when I looked at Pebbles and noticed his nose! Then I realised some of the other spots didn't look quite right, so I gave the dog a bath and took a closer look. We called him Pebbles because of his perfect spots and this dog has hardly any.

I took a moment to make a sketch of this lesser-spotted Pebbles imposter. Though a handsome dog, Mrs Tuft was right in her observation that it was shy and had very few spots.

And so I found myself taking the train once again down to Devon, where I was met at Grimpen Station by none other than Sir Henry Baskerville, who rode with me to Baskerville Hall in his carriage.

WITNESS STATEMENT — Sir Henry Baskerville

You must find this all very odd, Mr Holmes, after everything that happened here, but I felt it was time to bring some happiness back to the Hall. Being thought of as the former home of a demonic hound doesn't do much to encourage neighbours to stop by. Everyone in Grimpen loves dogs. We have a dog groomer in town, a dog breeder and even the head of the Kennel Association lives close by. It's been very successful over the past few years, but it's a lot of work, so when a gentleman from Pattock's Dog Treats offered to be a part of it, I couldn't say no.

I continued my conversation with Sir Henry in his study. When he stepped out to see about some refreshments, I took a look about his desk.

Join Sir Henry Baskerville and his hounds at the
🐾 Annual Baskerville Dog Show 🐾

WHEN: 28th April from 11 a.m.

WHERE: Baskerville Hall, Grimpen, Devon

This year's dog show is sponsored by
Pattock's Dog Treats – Premium Treats for Premium Pets –
and who best to judge the nation's finest dogs than the
makers of the nation's finest dog treats.

Those with dogs in the show are asked to arrive at the
grooming tent a half-hour before the show.

*Winners of each category will receive a year's supply of Pattock's Dog Treats,
and a free style and trim at Grimpen Groomer's after the show.*

Pattock's DOG TREATS

Dear Henry,

I can't tell you how happy I was to receive news that you had accepted our offer of sponsorship of your dog show.

This is our first year doing this sort of thing, so we are still finding our way a bit, but I think together we can host a great show and perhaps both make some money.

Very best wishes,

P. Pattock

Peter Pattock
Manager
Pattock's Dog Treats

Pattock's DOG TREATS

PREMIUM TREATS FOR PREMIUM PETS

For many owners, the family pet is just that, a part of the family, and as such deserves the very best treats money can buy. Keep your favourite poodle, terrier, Dalmatian or Labrador healthy and obedient with these delicious treats made from all natural meat and vegetable ingredients.

Look for the Pattock's Poodle to know you have chosen one of our award-winning treats.

KENNEL ASSOCIATION

Dear Sir Henry,

I am writing to you to tell you how utterly dismayed I was to discover that you have seen fit to allow the prestigious Baskerville Dog Show to fall into the money-grabbing hands of Mr Peter Pattock.

The Grimpen Chapter of the Kennel Association has always put on a wonderful show and attracted a high calibre of contestants.

Pattock may be able to offer the contestants prizes and is probably able to pay you a sizable sum, I do not doubt, but do they put the welfare of the dogs first? I think not if their junk-filled dog snacks are anything to go by.

I therefore regret to inform you that I have made the recommendation that any businesses that wish to remain affiliated with the Kennel Association withdraw their support for your show.

Thaddeus Crump

Thaddeus Crump
President of the Kennel Association

A strongly worded letter from the Kennel Association.

Reading that the winners of the show were all entitled to a free style and trim, I thought a trip to Grimpen Groomer's was in order. It is likely they may have been the last to see Pebbles before the switch took place.

We love dogs here in Grimpen. All shapes and sizes, pure breeds and mutts, not demonic hounds, mind. Ha ha! We've had quite enough of them.

I've been with the Kennel Association for years now. I love volunteering at the show. I wasn't going to let this little disagreement with Pattock's get in the way of helping out the owners. As a groomer, I keep up to date with all the new products. I even offer the winner in each category a free wash and brush-up after the show. Didn't get too close to this year's winner, though. Too shy. Lovely looking dog, though.

Dogs' Life Magazine

Meet... Mervin Spry

Dog show judge and breeder of fine pets.

SPRY, THE BREEDER
Dogs are my life as well as my livelihood. Here at Spry's Farm we breed only the finest puppies for the finest families. My experience as a competition judge means I know a good dog when I see one. Of course, you can never guarantee a dog will be a winner, but you can stack the odds in your favour. I specialise in matching just the right dog to just the right owner.

SPRY, THE JUDGE
I am not like the other judges. I like to get to know the dogs, which is why, during the finals, I insist on spending at least 15 minutes alone with each dog. Dogs can behave very differently without their owners. Well that's my way – the Spry way.

Hair dye for dogs?

A new brand of dog treat. Interesting.

🐾 GRIMPEN GROOMER'S • Appointment Book • APRIL

1	NO APPOINTMENTS - EM AT DS	9	NO APPOINTMENTS - EM AT DS	17		25	
2	NO APPOINTMENTS - EM AT DS	10		18		26	
3		11	PENNY (LABRADOR) - DYE 2 p.m.	19		27	
4	BRENDA (BASSET) - CLAW TRIM 3 p.m.	12		20		28	NO APPOINTMENTS - EM AT DS
5		13		21	NO APPOINTMENTS - EM AT DS	29	
6		14		22	NO APPOINTMENTS - EM AT DS	30	
7	NO APPOINTMENTS - EM AT DS	15	SUE (POODLE) - TRIM 9 a.m. ROVER (MUTT) - WASH 3 p.m.	23	NO APPOINTMENTS - EM AT DS		
8	NO APPOINTMENTS - EM AT DS	16		24			

My experience with hounds being that of the more demonic rather than pedigree variety, I thought a visit to the headquarters of the Kennel Association would be in order.

WITNESS STATEMENT	Thaddeus Crump

Don't get me wrong. We at the Kennel Association love a good dog show. Why wouldn't we? We love dogs and their owners and work hard every day to ensure our members' welfare. The affair at the Baskerville Dog Show is terrible. But it isn't the first. Look at this if you don't believe me.

Dog shows aren't just about which dog is the best and how many dog treats you can sell, it is about bringing the dog-owning community together and celebrating our beloved pets. Someone like Pattock could never understand that. I wonder with the scandals if he will be able to continue.

Crump handed me the latest Kennel Association newsletter.

KENNEL ASSOCIATION
NEWSLETTER

RUFF TIME FOR PATTOCK'S DOG TREATS

Spate of dognappings at recent dog shows associated with Pattock's Dog Treats leads Thaddeus Crump to urge all Kennel Association members to not enter their dogs in upcoming shows.

"Ask yourself, is a rosette and some free dog treats worth it?"

In the meantime, keep your eyes peeled for these prize pooches.

STORM - WINNER, BRIGHTON

DOGS REPORTED MISSING FOLLOWING A PATTOCK'S SHOW

Amadeus
Giant Poodle – Winner, Epsom and Dorking

Sparky
King Charles Spaniel – Runner-up, Manchester

Cocoa
Chocolate Labrador – 2nd Place, Newcastle

Hamish
West Highland Terrier – Winner, Glasgow

It would seem that Mervin Spry, breeder and judge, knows his dogs very well indeed. I went to see if I could find out more at his farm just outside Grimpen. Unfortunately, he was not home. Thankfully, I was able to speak with his wife, a Mrs Geneva Spry.

WITNESS STATEMENT	Mrs Geneva Spry

An honour, Mr Holmes! I'm afraid Mervin is away at the moment. He has been away every weekend since he started with the shows. It's such a shame, I hardly see him what with him having to travel all over the country. "Never marry an ambitious man," my mother said. "He might think he's going places, but you can't be sure he'll take you with him." She was a wise woman. Here I am, left to look after all these dogs and their babies. You think real babies are hard work. There are more than 20 puppies on the farm at the moment. They certainly keep me on my toes and every other week it seems he brings home another. It's worse than the local pound what with all the yapping and growling.

Just last week he brought home a spotty one. I'd told him - no more! So, I took it down to the pound. That'll show him. When I say no more, I mean no more!

If you'll excuse me, Mr Holmes, I think I just saw the peddler passing the end of the lane. I must stop him and buy some black boot polish. I was sure I'd bought some just the other week. I cannot think where it has all gone. You can take a look at Mervin's schedule if you like.

Spry is quite the collector.

Pattock's
Mervin Spry Show Schedule: APRIL

1 DOG SHOW – NEWCASTLE

2

3

4

5

6

7

8 DOG SHOWS – BOLTON / MANCHESTER

9

10

11

12

13

14

15 DOG SHOWS – EPSOM / DORKING

16

17

18

19

20 DOG SHOW – GLASGOW

21 DOG SHOW – EDINBURGH

22

23

24

25

26

27

28 DOG SHOW – BASKERVILLE HALL

29

30

Mr Mervin Spry
Spry's Farm
Grimpen

Dear Mr Spry,

Thank you for your interest in our dog. We think he is very special, so it is always nice when you hear that someone else does, too.

I am afraid I will have to decline your offer. My wife loves the daft mutt dearly and will not be parted from him for even a moment. It would therefore be more than my life is worth to sell him.

Yours regretfully,
C. Tuft

🐾 GRIMPEN GROOMER'S

Items purchased:	
4 lb. Wagger's Wafers	
TOTAL DUE	4s 6d

Could this spotty dog mentioned by Mrs Spry be the prizewinning Dalmatian, Pebbles? I hurried to the Baskerville Pound. I couldn't be sure if any of them were Pebbles. I started to see spots! I did take a moment to take a quick sketch of each spotty dog. There were six in total.

Do any of them look familiar to you?

Dog 1

Dog 2

Dog 3

Dog 4

Dog 5

Dog 6

It was a happy moment
when numbers 2 and 6
came up to lick my hand.
Such friendly animals.

A curious case of dognapping.
Let us examine the evidence further:

1. When could Pebbles have been restyled?

2. Why does Thaddeus Crump not like Pattock's Dog Treats?

3. When could the other dogs have gone missing?

4. What happened to Mrs Spry's shoe polish?

5. A couple of the dogs from the pound are very similar. Could either of them be Pebbles?

Time to reflect on the evidence.

Discover the truth about Pebbles' disappearance by holding the opposite page against a mirror.

Well done, reader! With your help, the reputation of the Baskerville Dog Show and Pattock's Dog Treats will be restored.

The culprit in this case, as you correctly deduced, was none other than Mervin Spry, dog breeder and judge. He used his position as a prestigious judge to get close to some of the finest pets in the land and couldn't resist adding them to his collection with a view to breeding show winners.

Ellen Molesworth, although she had access to the dogs, did not get the chance to groom 'Pebbles'. She was unable get close to him because he was too shy. He was too shy because he had already been switched for the imposter by Mervin Spry during the final judging. Ellen also was not at the Epsom and Dorking dog shows when the prizewinning poodle went missing.

People will pay a high price for a fine dog and thanks to your hard work that high price will not be paid by Mrs Tuft, who will now have her beloved Pebbles back home again after his adventure at the pound.

The Forger and the Fake

A picture-perfect crime was brought to my attention at Baker Street today when a distressed gallery owner, Raymond DeQuincy, entered my apartment.

WITNESS STATEMENT	Raymond DeQuincy

I have been assured there has been the gravest of thefts from my gallery and yet I can't say when or where it took place. To celebrate a new masterpiece I acquired - 'The Reflection of a Fine Lady' by Edouard Toulone - I invited a select group of critics to come to an advanced viewing before the public unveiling on Friday. The picture was a favourite of mine and my brother's when we were at art school, having been invited by the artist to view it in his home.

All was going well and the critics were admiring the fine painting, when Gr... Edmund Granger, critic at the *Evening Herald*, arrived. He took one look at the painting and pronounced it a fake. I know not what to do! I borrowed money to acquire this picture, only to discover that it is worthless. Please, Sherlock, I've checked my papers and the picture I purchased was the original, I'm sure, so it must have been switched. I can't see any differences between the one I brought home with me from the Toulone estate and the one on the wall of the gallery. Please help, Sherlock, I could lose everything!

Helpfully, the distressed Raymond had brought with him the certificate of authenticity.

Certificate of Authenticity

'The Reflection of a Fine Lady' by Edouard Toulone, 1880

Portrait of a well-dressed lady as she looks into an ornate mirror at her dressing table. The unknown lady wears a blue silk dress and a single glove; the other lays upon her lap. On her dressing table is a vase of day lilies. The dress is notable for its bold use of the rare and expensive lapis lazuli pigment – a colour so intensely blue it was given the Latin name ultramarine, meaning 'beyond the ocean'.

ARTWORK AUTHENTICITY ASSOCIATION

ARTWORK AUTHENTICITY ASSOCIATION
• 16 Row Avenue, London •

RECORD OF SALE

Purchased from the private estate of Edouard Toulone.

I confirm this work was painted by Edouard Toulone.

Signed
Marcel Toulone
Marcel Toulone
Son of the artist

APPROVED

Authenticated by the son of the artist. It would appear Raymond did purchase the original painting.

My first stop: the scene of the alleged crime - the Strand Studios Gallery near the Embankment. Here are a few of the items I picked up:

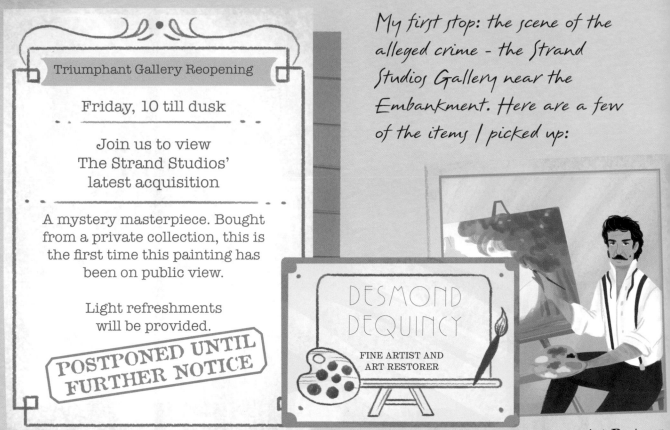

DESMOND DEQUINCY

FINE ARTIST AND
ART RESTORER

Desmond DeQuincy - Art Restorer

I made enquiries with the guard situated outside.

WITNESS STATEMENT	Ken Fenton - security guard

It's a bit embarrassing really. The painting arrived last week and there's been one of us outside every day and night since. We thought we were here to protect something priceless, but now we hear it's a worthless fake. It's a fine picture of a beautiful lady, if you ask me, but what would I know? What I do know is that nobody has come in or out without having their bag searched and neither myself nor any of my fellow constables have seen anyone sneaking out with a priceless painting tucked under their arm. We would have noticed.

A fine picture indeed. The door has been watched. When did the theft take place?

A letter was left at the reception desk for Raymond.
I took the liberty of opening it:

Dearest brother,

I wrote as soon as I heard the news.

It *would* have to be Grumpy Granger to expose the fraud. He's always been after a big scoop. I am sorry it was at your considerable expense. What a blow to your fine gallery! I was looking forward to seeing your mystery acquisition.

I would love to meet with you and discuss what you wish to do with the space now it has become available. I have some ideas I would like to share.

Yours,
Dessy

Raymond DeQuincy
Strand Studios Gallery
Embankment
London

An ambitious brother.
How far would he go to get his own work into a gallery? He has some interesting skills.

Could 'Grumpy Granger' be after more than a big scoop?

Condolences to you

Ray, old friend. Very sorry about all this. It's a lovely painting. It's just not the original. Perhaps if you'd paid a bit more attention in art history... Ha ha! Sorry. Of course, I'm going to have to write about it. Again, sorry.

To make amends, I could take a closer look at it for you. See if we can track down the forger. Do you think you could bring it to my apartment? I shouldn't need more than a day. I may not be able to do anything, of course, but there's so much we know now about the colours and strokes used by artists, I may be able to identify the villain just by taking a closer look.

Shall we say tomorrow? Do let me know. I'd so much like to make amends for the unavoidable harm I have caused you.

Ed Granger

I took a look around the gallery. The painting was indeed a fine one, as the guard observed. I took a photograph so as to compare it to the description once I had returned to Baker Street:

'The Reflection of a Fine Lady'

Edouard Toulone
1880

This is to certify that

Raymond DeQuincy

attended the St Dunstan's
School of Art, London

with 1st class honours and a distinction
in Art History

St Dunstan's School of Art

I then went to investigate Raymond's office to see if there was anything that could help us.

This is to certify that

Desmond DeQuincy

attended the St Dunstan's
School of Art, London

with 1st class honours and a distinction
in Copying and Art Restoration

St Dunstan's School of Art

Dear Raymond,

We hope this letter finds you well, though how you can be well given the neglect you have shown your brother we do not know.

We are asking, no, we are URGING you, please give dearest Dessy a chance and let him exhibit his work in your gallery. When we funded this venture, we had hoped it would be an opportunity for you both.

Please do not make us regret this decision. Dessy is becoming quite desperate.

Yours lovingly,

Mother and Father

For Dessy.

1st class. Grumpy Granger isn't going to be happy about that!

Well done, little brother!

Just how desperate is Dessy?

Curious about Raymond's artist brother, I took my leave of the gallery and walked to his brother's studio in Covent Garden. The artist was out, but his landlord allowed me to look around.

Dear Brother,

I'm sure it must be very frustrating for you seeing me with the successful gallery while you struggle to find a place to display your art.

The gallery is in its early days. I am hoping one day it will be the talk of the town with a fine reputation. Then, and only then, will I display your work so that it can get the attention it deserves. I can only ask you to trust me.

Yours sincerely,
Ray

PS I have acquired a new 'mystery' painting. I think you will like it. It's not been on view to the public before. On 'reflection', I think it will cause quite a stir! You will not believe it when you see it – I think you know it rather well.

The painting did cause quite the stir, but not the kind Raymond imagined.

Raymond asks his brother to trust him, but can we trust Dessy?

With warmest thanks

The painting is quite extraordinary.
Your skill as a copyist is great, indeed.

It is a painting of a quality such that
I had never had a hope of owning.

I enclose a cheque for £8.

Yours most gratefully,
Godred Mengran

I spotted this thank-you note for Desmond's latest commission, signed from a rather odd name.

NEWMAN & CO
FINE ART SUPPLIES
17 GERRARD ST, LONDON

ITEM	PRICE
Oil paints:	
Dragon's blood	
Mummy brown	
~~Lapis lazuli~~	
~~Synthetic ultramarine~~	
Indian yellow	£3 70d

Dessy, this was put on your account which is now in excess of £20. We would be most grateful if you could pay this at your earliest convenience.

Dessy is a skilled copyist with expensive taste in paints.

5TH JUNE

ALAS! I HAVE MASTERED THE GREAT MASTERS. COPYING IS NO CHALLENGE FOR ME ANY MORE. MY LATEST WAS SO CLOSE TO AN ORIGINAL I HAD STUDIED AT ST DUNSTAN'S, THAT TO MAKE SURE IT WAS NOT MISTAKEN FOR IT, I INCLUDED SOME DELIBERATE ERRORS. MY PERSONAL COPYIST CODE OF CONDUCT. ONLY AN EXPERT WOULD BE ABLE TO SEE MY HAND IN HER CREATION.

AN ODD COMMISSION. I NEVER MET THE FELLOW IT WAS FOR, AS HE INSISTED I LEAVE IT AT THE DESK AT THE SAVOY. IT SHOULD GO SOME SMALL WAY TO COVER MY MANY DEBTS. HE MADE NO MENTION OF THE BLUES.

IF ONLY MY BROTHER WOULD FULFIL HIS PROMISE TO EXHIBIT MY WORK INSTEAD OF THIS 'NEW PAINTING' HE IS SO PLEASED WITH.

ONE DAY, I WILL SHOW HIM WHAT I CAN DO AND HE WILL BE SORRY.

I called in on Edmund Granger, the critic who declared Raymond's painting a fake.

WITNESS STATEMENT	Edmund Granger

I feel for Raymond, I really do. We were good friends in art school, though we ran with different crowds. I think Ray may even have thought himself a better artist. He certainly thinks he's had more success what with his gallery. It doesn't matter that the London art world hangs on my every word. As I said, I feel for Raymond, but it was so obviously a fake it would cost my reputation to have it otherwise.

I asked Edmund if I could see some of his most celebrated articles and he was keen to oblige. While he went into another room to look for them, I took a quick look around.

On his desk, I found this interesting receipt:

SAVOY
STRAND

Afternoon tea for one.

TOTAL   5s 6d

I sketched the covers of a couple of intriguing books in Granger's apartment:

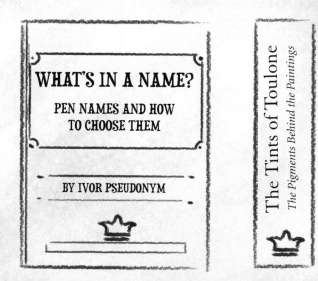

WHAT'S IN A NAME?

PEN NAMES AND HOW TO CHOOSE THEM

BY IVOR PSEUDONYM

The Tints of Toulone
The Pigments Behind the Paintings

EVENING HERALD

LONDON'S DAILY NEWS   10th JUNE

Strand Studios Acquires Fake

Reported by Edmund Granger

As London's most well-loved art critic, I find myself invited to some of the most glamorous gallery openings and previews.

Raymond DeQuincy, owner of Strand Studio Gallery and fellow survivor of St Dunstan's School of Art, was keen to show off a new painting he had acquired to a very select group.

It pains me to tell you, dear reader, that Raymond and the select gathering's excitement was for nought. The painting is a fake. It takes a keen eye to spot a forgery in this modern age and as the owner of a pair of such eyes, I can tell you that they are a curse as much as they are a blessing.

How I would like to extol the virtues of this masterpiece, and I will admit it is a counterfeit of no mean skill. It is breathtaking. But if you wish to see the original 'Reflection of a Fine Lady' by Edouard Toulone, do not go to Strand Studios, for it is not there. Where it might be remains a mystery.

ARTIST REVIEW MONTHLY   ISSUE 94

Meet the Critic

NAME: Edmund Granger

QUALIFICATIONS: 2nd Class Degree from St Dunstan's School of Fine Art

LOVES: Great paintings, gallery openings and meeting artists.

DREAMS: To own a genuine masterpiece and to see it hanging in his home.

Edmund had rather modestly framed another article and left some copies underneath — I assume for his guests to take.

While examining the frame of this article, I adjusted it slightly and as I did so, the wall it was mounted on moved to the side to reveal something of great interest. Edmund's dreams of owning a great masterpiece may already have been realised. I took a photograph:

This painting bears a striking likeness to the one hanging in Raymond's gallery. I suggest we take a closer look in order to ascertain which masterpiece is in fact the original.

PLEASE ENSURE DELIVERY TO GODRED MENGRAN.

I found this note lying on the ground beneath the painting.

Also beneath the painting were a selection of brushes and a piece of canvas:

GENUINE LAPIS LAZULI

SYNTHETIC ULTRAMARINE

A mysterious case indeed. Let us brush up on the evidence with some questions to focus the mind:

1. How does the description of the painting compare to the one in the gallery?

2. How could the painting get past Ken Fenton and the other security guards?

3. To what degree is Edmund Granger jealous of the DeQuincys?

4. Can you untangle the mystery of Godred Mengran?

5. Can you tell which painting is the original?

Much as the lady in the painting gazes into the mirror, so must you.

Hold the opposite page to a mirror to discover the truth behind the forgery.

Congratulations, reader! After reviewing the evidence I so diligently gathered, you have discovered who is responsible for the theft of this painting. No one… yet. There has been no crime, though the damage to the reputation of the Strand Studio Gallery may be irreparable.

Although desperate to exhibit his work in his brother's gallery, Desmond did not steal the painting. In fact, he did not know which painting his brother had acquired before its theft was announced. Raymond had wanted to keep that as a surprise, as it was a favourite of theirs from art school. Had Raymond told his brother, Desmond would have revealed that he was more familiar with the painting than even he knew, having painted a copy of it from memory for a mysterious client, 'Godred Mengran,' - an oddly named chap who he had never met. Or had he? Look closely at the name. Godred Mengran, as you had undoubtedly already deduced, is none other than Edmund Granger.

Granger's offer to examine Raymond DeQuincy's 'fake,' was not him trying to make amends at all, but rather his chance to switch the painting he bought from Desmond and keep the original for himself.

The Poisoned Apprentice

The owner of a very fine silver-topped cane visited me at my rooms in Baker Street – a Mr Samuel Barker of the newly named Barker & Co. He was in a state of some agitation.

BARKER & CO.
Best Silver
Kirby Street, London

Finest Designs, Finest Repairs, Finest Antiques
—— **Sterling Silver** ——

I took a photo of Barker's cane.

Indeed, it was turning a most curious shade of orange.

Mr Holmes, I fear I may have made a terrible mistake. Though, I'm not sure how or where. The problem I come to you with is that of my apprentice, who has taken sick all of a sudden. He's only 20 years old, and in a short space of time has gone from a vigorous and healthy young man to one who is constantly dizzy and short of breath. He became so bad that he has taken to his bed. Imagine that!

And now my business is suffering, too. For many years we have had a sterling reputation, if you'll pardon the pun, for producing and repairing some of the finest pieces of silver in the land, and since Stanley joined me, business has got better and better, but good business makes for jealous rivals. Customers are returning things almost every day saying the quality isn't what it was. I had a look myself and it isn't. Look at my cane. It's turned orange! Why would it turn orange? I can only think this is the work of a jealous competitor messing with our work.

My nephew, Patrick, blames Stanley, says he has no loyalty, but I can't believe that. Stanley is a real perfectionist. He won't let a jug or teapot leave the shop without checking the pour from it - he can't abide a dribbly spout.

I started as an apprentice myself, so I was keen to take one on when I could. Thanks be to St Gerard's, I found perhaps the greatest apprentice one could ever hope for. He was an errand boy with few prospects. Now, he has the world at his feet, with companies desperate for him to work for them.

I took in my nephew to help out my brother-in-law, Monty, who is a silversmith up in Birmingham. They had fallen out, but he was keen to stay in the trade, and with Stanley about to leave, it seemed like a good time.

Please, Mr Holmes, help me to save both my apprentice and my business before it's too late.

I took a trip to Barker & Co. to see for myself what was going on. One thing that stood out to me on approaching the store was the window display. It was somewhat haphazard.

See this sketch to observe my meaning. Using what little I know of silver, I have also noted the year I believe each piece to have been made. It was very odd indeed.

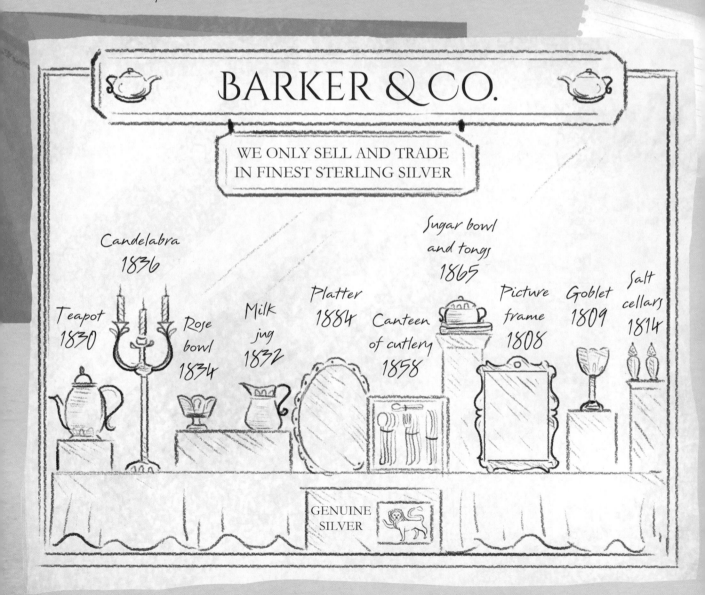

BARKER & CO.

WE ONLY SELL AND TRADE
IN FINEST STERLING SILVER

Candelabra
1836

Sugar bowl
and tongs
1865

Teapot
1830

Rose
bowl
1834

Milk
jug
1832

Platter
1884

Canteen
of cutlery
1858

Picture
frame
1808

Goblet
1809

Salt
cellars
1814

GENUINE
SILVER

Samuel being out when I called, I questioned his nephew about the curious window arrangement.

WITNESS STATEMENT   Patrick Brigham

The window? Oh! that is Stan's doing. He has some funny ideas. You wouldn't get away with that kind of display in Birmingham, I can tell you. They keep their windows tidy up there. They have standards. I'll take a look after you leave, Mr Holmes; though whenever I move things around, Stan moves them back to exactly where they were before. He should know his place, but Uncle Sam has a bit of a soft spot for him. He'll be gone soon, to some fancy place or other. We will be well rid. I won't be having an apprentice when I have my own shop. More trouble than they are worth, sticking their beak in when it's not wanted, checking your work when it's not their place. No thank you. When I have enough cash to have my own place, I will not be having an apprentice.

That moment, a customer came into the shop...

WITNESS STATEMENT   Customer Statement

I'm afraid I'm going to have to return this teapot. It pours wonderfully, but see here it's turning the most curious shade of orange.

I asked to see all the articles that had been returned to the shop. They all had the following mark:

I asked to be allowed to see this famous apprentice in his room above the shop. The poor young man was in a sorry state indeed. He was sleeping and seemed as though he needed the rest. His room was able to offer me some information.

London School of Silversmiths

COURSES - JANUARY 1892

Silver plate looks just as great!

Starts: 23rd Janaury, 6 weeks

Get the look of silver at a fraction of the cost with the newest in electroplated silver or EPNS.

How to use potassium cyanide (KCN) and an electrical current to turn copper into silver.

Find out more from Montgomery Brigham from Brigham's of Birmingham

Making your mark

Starts: 18th Janaury, 1 day

A look at hallmarks and what they mean.

Find out more from London Assay Office

Does Stanley want to learn about silver plate? Those are some terrible ingredients.

Marshall & Bouche

Dear Stanley,

We would dearly like to offer you a position on completion of your apprenticeship at Barker & Co. We will also be able to offer you a comfortable apartment.

We at Marshall & Bouche know that we are not the only ones aware of your prodigious talent, and would be prepared to meet and exceed any offer that was made to you by one of our competitors. We will go to any length to get you to come and work for us.

Yours hopefully,

Vincent Bouche

Vincent Bouche

LAPIN & FOX
14 UPPER DRIVE, LONDON

Dear Stanley,

We are writing to you to tell you of an opening at Lapin & Fox as head of our design room. It would be an unprecedented step to install a newly-qualified apprentice as head of design, but having seen examples of your work and the sketches you brought with you to our showroom, we feel confident that you will rise to the challenge.

As regards to salary, we are open to your recommendation. What value would you put on your labour? We value it very highly indeed. We have heard all is not well at Barker & Co. so we would compel you to make this decision quickly, before your reputation becomes as tarnished as Barker's silver.

Yours expectantly,
Henry Fox

PETERSHAM AND WILLS
SILVER ROAD WORKSHOPS, LONDON E1

Dear Stanley,

We hear of difficult times at Barker & Co. Perhaps it would be best to leave before your apprenticeship is up. Barker is going down - it would be terrible if your treasure of a talent were to be taken with it.

We would like to offer you a position, if you decide to leave soon. Some free advice: the longer you stay, the less we or anyone else will be likely to pay.

Peter Petersham

I took the liberty of opening this letter as it only arrived this morning:

Dear Stanley,

I regret to inform you that we are no longer able to offer you a position at Marshall & Bouche.

News has reached us of sinister goings-on at Barker & Co., rumours of counterfeit goods and shoddy work. While I realise this is almost certainly not your fault, we cannot take the risk at this time.

Yours regretfully,

Vincent Bouche

Vincent Bouche

An apprentice with fine prospects indeed. How far would the competition be willing to go?

1st January
Poor Mr Barker will be heartbroken when he hears of the betrayal going on under his very nose by someone he trusts like a son. His kindness is repaid with the loss of both his reputation and business.

Inside Stanley's sketchbook were a number of designs for his maker's mark:

This one!

I decided to pay a call to Stanley's physician to see if he could shed any light on his mysterious condition.

WITNESS STATEMENT — Doctor Lancett

It's a curious case, Mr Holmes. No sign of infection or symptoms of any natural disease I have seen before. I can only think he may have been poisoned in some way. But who would wish to poison such a young man? Without knowing what could have poisoned him, I'm not sure how best to treat him.

DOCTOR REPORT

DOCTOR NAME: Dr Lancett

PATIENT NAME: Stanley Shaw

NOTES

20-year-old male suffering from a sudden onset of dizziness and shortness of breath. Unable to work and either unable or unwilling to explain how he came to be in such a predicament. Patient is not familiar to the physician owing to having been in perfect health up until very recently.

A suspected poisoning? Sinister work indeed.

I consulted Watson's medical books and found this interesting entry. I do wish he wouldn't handle his books with inky hands...

Common Poisons
• Symptoms and Where to Find Them •

COMPOUNDS OF STRYCHNINE
Symptoms
Muscle pain, agitation.
Sore neck and back.

Found in pesticides used in agriculture.

COMPOUNDS OF CYANIDE
Symptoms
Weakness, sleepiness, shortness of breath and dizziness.

Found in

ARSENIC
Symptoms
Stomach pain, vomiting, hair loss, diarrhoea.

Found in rat poison and used in the bronzing process.

HEMLOCK
Symptoms
Vomiting, trembling and paralysis.

Naturally occurring plant found on riverbanks and roadsides.

Do any of these symptoms match those of our ailing apprentice? Could he really be suffering the effects of poisoning?

Something about the marks Stanley was designing made me want to know more about what the marks on silver mean. The London Assay Office keeps a record of all the marks engraved on precious metals. I thought they might be able to give me more information. What I learned was very interesting.

The lion shows the silver is sterling, as in genuine.

The final mark is the maker's mark.

The leopard head shows that it was made in London. An anchor in this spot would indicate Birmingham.

The letter represents the date. Each item of silver is marked with a letter indicating the year in which it is made. Every year there is a new letter and when all the letters have been used, 'A' is used again but in a different typeface.

The next mark is the head of the monarch who was on the throne when the item was made.

What interested me most was the date stamp.
An interesting code of conduct.

I took this sheet to show the various letters and typefaces used:

How would we now appraise the arrangement in Barker & Co.'s window? A display can say a lot.

It appears that Stanley is a friend of the Assay Office. He clearly knows his dates.

TONIGHT'S TALK
Making the most of your apprenticeship
with Stanley Shaw

POSTPONED INDEFINITELY

I headed to the nephew's apartment. What can we learn about this newcomer from where he lives?

Brigham's
of Birmingham

Dear Patrick,

I hope this letter finds you well and that you have settled in with my brother-in-law.

I will be in town on Saturday talking about the work I have been doing. I do hope you can make it. You could perhaps learn something; though I'm sure you think you know it all already. Your mother claims you ran before you could walk and that's been your way with everything.

Make sure you are listening to your uncle. You can learn a lot from him.

With love,
M. Brigham

On Patrick's desk, I discovered these brass dyes for stamping – I used them with a little ink to get a closer look:

A B C D E F
G H I J K L
M N O P Q R
S T U V W
X Y Z

What can we deduce from this curious scene? What indeed has Patrick been doing?

A genuinely concerning case. Study the questions
below before reaching your conclusion:

1. Who would benefit from Barker & Co.'s downfall?

2. Do you notice anything curious about the maker's mark on the
returned silver pieces?

3. Who is Montgomery Brigham and does he have any special skills?

4. Which symptoms of poisoning most closely match those of Stanley?

5. Do you notice anything curious about the dates of the pieces in the
window display?

With hope, our
investigation will
save the reputation
of Barker & Co.
and perhaps even
the life of Stanley.

Discover the truth by
holding the opposite
page up to a mirror.

Well done, reader!

Your solid detective work has revealed that the nephew, Patrick Brigham, is not sterling but is in fact a forger and an accidental poisoner. His crime was not one of malice but one of deception and haste. Patrick was sent to London by his father for trying to run before he could walk. His father, Montgomery Brigham of Birmingham, is a pioneer in silver plating, a skill Patrick believes he knows all about.

In an effort to raise money to start his own shop, Patrick has been plating cheaper metal items such as copper with silver and passing them off as the real thing.

To do this, metal items need to have an electrical current passed through them and be dipped in a solution of potassium cyanide [KCN] and potassium silver cyanide [KAg(CN)$_2$]. The electricity passing through the metal causes the silver in the solution to stick to the outside of the item, giving it the look of solid silver.

In Patrick's haste, he did not rinse a teapot thoroughly before putting it in the shop and so when Stanley poured himself a cup of tea from it (to check how it poured), the tea was laced with cyanide.

Patrick's hastiness at using electroplating before fully understanding the process meant that the items lost their silvery appearance after only a few uses.

To cover his tracks, he used a set of brass dyes to mark his forged pieces with Stanley's stamp, but as you probably noticed, his brass dyes were unable to make a crisp mark.

The Adventure of the Found Finger

One of the most gruesome clues I have come across greeted me on the steps to my rooms in Baker Street yesterday: a severed finger in a blood-soaked handkerchief. I have scoured the papers and enquired with Inspector LeStrade regarding any open cases where a finger has been reported missing; it is not something that would go unnoticed, after all. I can only deduce that the owner of the finger must also be missing or indeed dead.

Dr Watson being absent, I presented the finger to another medical acquaintance Dr Terrence Sprenkle.

Diagnosis Report

Doctor name: Doctor T. Sprenkle

Date of diagnosis: 8th June

Diagnosis:

Left little finger. Dark hair on lower portion suggests the owner is male. Flesh at point of amputation suggests finger was severed quickly with a very sharp, heavy object. I would speculate a meat cleaver or guillotine.

Other observations:

Skin on finger is smooth and without callouses, suggesting the owner is not used to manual work. Ink smudged on finger suggests owner may be left-handed or works in the printing trade. Distinctive signet ring with attractive heart design.

More information was needed and so I placed an advertisement for a found ring in the local newspaper. The ring was so distinctive that I felt sure that someone would recognise it and be able to connect me with its owner.

I gave no clue as to its gory contents.

– FOUND –

Signet ring with distinctive heart-shaped design. Keen to return.

Contact S. Holmes, 221b Baker St if you are, or you have information regarding, the owner of this ring.

Reader, the advert proved a success. For the next morning, while I was out attending to another case, a Mr Hart came to enquire about the ring. He left a calling card and so I went to speak with him at his place of work. On arrival, a quick glance at this well-dressed man's left hand made it very clear that although he recognised the ring, he was certainly not its last wearer.

· HART BROTHERS' ·
BANK
FAMILY FINANCIALS
15 WARDEN AVENUE, LONDON

WITNESS STATEMENT	Ronald Hart

How grateful I am that you have found my signet ring. I will be delighted to have it returned. I would be happy to offer you a substantial reward for its return and also for information regarding how it came to be in your possession. It is vitally important that I know more on this, as it could help my family to recover other lost items.

Unhappy with his clearly dishonest answer, I produced the ring with the finger still inside. This seemed to elicit a more genuine response.

On seeing the finger, Ronald produced two letters he had recently received.

WE have Your BROTHER.

Do WHAT WE want

or we will return

HIM to you

PIECE BY PIECE.

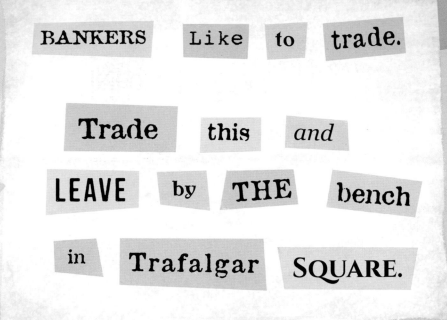

BANKERS Like to trade.

Trade this and

LEAVE by THE bench

in Trafalgar SQUARE.

This last letter was left with the most curious thing – a briefcase filled with bloodstained banknotes.

Something other than gore stood out to me about these bloodied bills.

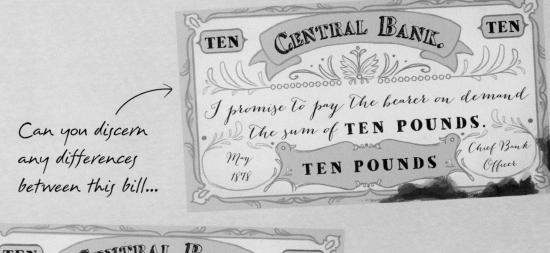

Can you discern any differences between this bill...

TEN   CENTRAL BANK.   TEN

I promise to pay the bearer on demand the sum of TEN POUNDS.

May 1878   TEN POUNDS   Chief Bank Officer

TEN   CENTRAL BANK   TEN

I promise to pay the bearer on demand the sum of TEN POUNDS.

May 1879   TEN POUNDS   Chief Bank Officer

... and one from my own pocket?

I asked Ronald to show me in to his brother's office to get an idea of the man we are looking for. What do you make of what I found? Perhaps some of this will come in useful later... I cannot tell.

1st June

Things are getting out of hand. I am going to have to think of a way to pay everyone or suffer the consequences. If I could just pick one winner. What was it Father used to say? "You make your own luck." Well if I can't make my own luck, perhaps I can make something else.

People I owe:

Dupe's Gaming House, Jermyn St - £200

Feinstein's Fine Inks and Papers - £400

Dryden & Co. Debt Collectors - £300

D. Andrew - Loss at bridge - £40

G. Edwards - Loss at hazard - £30

EPSOM DERBY

2 JUNE, 1890

Surefoot rider
Fred Barrett

£300 at 40/95

3RD JUNE

Surefoot a Sure Bet?

Sainfoin wins the 1890 Epsom Derby. An outsider, not expected to place, sped across the finishing line, leaving the bookies' favourite, Surefoot, in 4th place.

Sainfoin's proud owner, Sir James Miller, commented following the race, "I'm delighted! Though there will be a lot of people owing people money. Never bet what you can't afford to lose is my motto. Or better yet, bet on Sainfoin!"

In the centre of the desk, left as though someone wanted it to be found, was this code with the note attached:

HART BROTHERS' BANK

HART BROTHERS' BANK
Where brothers can bank on each other.

Banking brothers code:

A	B	C	D	E	F	G	H	I	J	K	L	M
^	1	*	2	X	3	=	4	!	5	>	6	-

N	O	P	Q	R	S	T	U	V	W	X	Y	Z
7	±	8	&	9	\	0	<	~	+	%	{	}

WITNESS STATEMENT   Ronald Hart

Happy times indeed. I don't know where he must have found this. We would play bankers when we were kids and pretend we were just like Father. We'd pass notes to each other in our own code. Ha! We thought we were so clever.

Reggie would appear to have been playing a dangerous game and an expensive one at that. Perhaps a visit to where these games were played will shed some light on the player's whereabouts.

WITNESS STATEMENT   Kenneth Dupe - Gaming House owner

We get all sorts in here from fine fellows on their way from their clubs to your average working man. Nothing beats a good gamble to get your heart racing. A lot say they come here to unwind, even more leave more wound up than when they arrived.

Hart… I know him. Yes. Here a lot. Less so lately and I'm not surprised. He owes a lot of people a lot of money. Apparently he owns a bank or something. You wouldn't know it the way he owes people. He tried to pay me, but I wasn't having any of it.

People come looking for him all the time, but they won't find him. I doubt I'll see him again. His money isn't good here any more.

Someone was in just the other day - they left these letters for him…

I noticed an interesting sign up at the door.

Gamblers beware:
Can't pay? Don't play!

WE TAKE CASH, CHEQUES, JEWELLERY, PROPERTY AND IF NONE OF THE ABOVE IS AVAILABLE WE WILL TAKE WHATEVER YOU HOLD DEAR.

YOU THROW THE DICE,
YOU PAY THE PRICE!

I took the letters addressed to Reginald. It seems I am not the only person looking for him...

FEINSTEIN'S FINE PAPERS
— FOR YOUR FINE PAPER NEEDS —

With compliments

Hart, I need to be paid

214 CHARING CROSS ROAD, LONDON

Dryden & Co.
Debt Collectors

Dear Reg,

I see you had a hard day at the track.

We need to be paid, Reg. Find a way or we will be forced to get nasty.

We will visit you at work where we will 'bank' on getting paid.

Signed,
M. Dryden

I decided to follow the paper trail, or rather the calling card, and visited Feinstein's Fine Papers. I am surprised I had not visited before — their papers were very fine indeed. Reader, help me make sense of what I found there.

WITNESS STATEMENT   Gustav Feinstein

I know Hart. I have gambled with him many times. He is not good at it. I hope he is better at banking. He owes me money. I lent him some at the hazard table. I assume you've spoken to Kenneth at the Gaming House. He owes a lot of people money, most of them more dangerous than me. I'm not surprised he's missing. Debts need to be paid.

I asked to see some of their new designs of writing paper. I have to write many letters and like to use a high-quality paper. While Feinstein went to get it, I took a look at the order book.

One large order stood out:

FEINSTEIN'S FINE PAPERS
— CUSTOMER ORDER BOOK —

DATE	ITEMS	DELIVERY	PAYMENT
6th June	Guillotine Printing press Ink Cotton paper	460a Jermyn Street	Cash on delivery promised. Was told to return for payment at the end of the day. Now paid in full.

FEINSTEIN'S FINE PAPERS
— ORDER CONFIRMATION —

DATE: 6th June

ITEMS: Guillotine
Printing press
Ink
Cotton paper

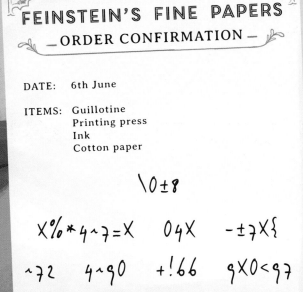

$\setminus 0 \pm 8$

$X\% * 4 \wedge 7 = X \qquad 04X \qquad - \pm 7X\{$

$\wedge 72 \qquad 4 \wedge 90 \qquad + !66 \qquad 9X0 < 97$

It was then that I noticed some curious marks on the order slip that acknowledged receipt of the order.

Reader, can you make sense of this?
Where have we seen marks like this before?

Feinstein returned with some fine paper. I bought a large quantity, as I have a lot of letters to reply to every day.

I paid and received this banknote in return.

Does it look familiar to you?

TEN   **Central Bank.**   **TEN**

I promise to pay the bearer on demand the sum of **TEN POUNDS.**

May 1878

TEN POUNDS

Chief Bank Officer

I took a walk to the address of the recipient of Feinstein's mysterious order.
A bloody scene awaited me.

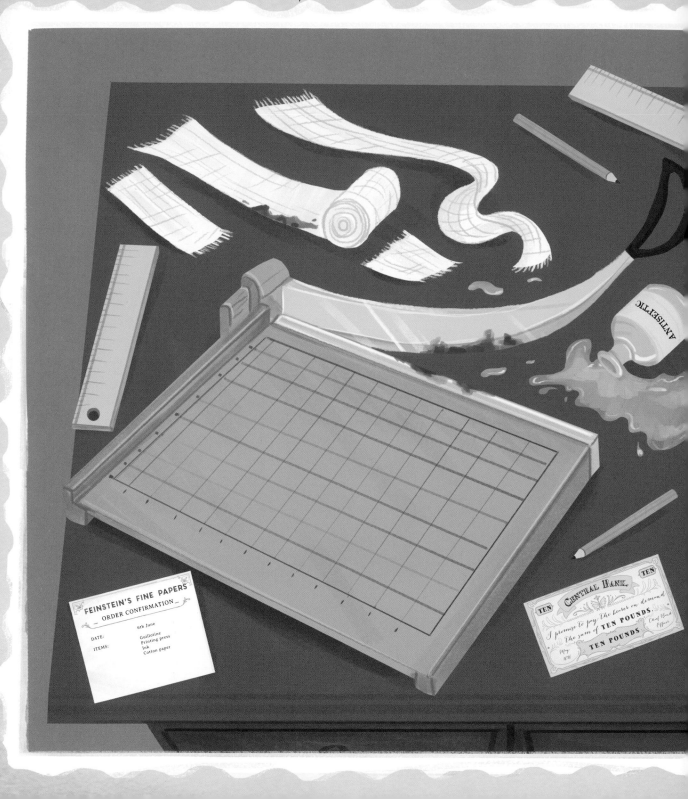

A severed finger has led us on quite the gruesome journey. Consider these queries before you submit your solution:

1. Why are the banknotes different to those in Sherlock's wallet?

2. To whom does Reggie owe the most money?

3. Why was Reggie's money refused by Kenneth Dupe?

4. Can you make sense of the mysterious note on Feinstein's receipt?

5. Are you able to deduce how the finger was detached?

Central Bank.
TEN   TEN
I promise to pay the bearer on demand
The sum of **TEN POUNDS**.
May
1878   **TEN POUNDS**   Chief Bank Officer

Central Bank
TEN   TEN
I promise to pay the bearer on demand
The sum of **TEN POUNDS**.
May
1879   **TEN POUNDS**   Chief Bank Officer

If you can stomach the truth of this terrible case, hold the opposite page to a mirror.

Reader, your calculations are correct. The crime was not the severed finger, nor the kidnapping of a dear brother, nor even the non-payment of debts. This was a crime of forgery and attempted money laundering.

Reginald Hart was a gambler and an unwise one at that. He owed lots of people lots of money and some of them not very nice. How could he pay? The bank is filled with money, but his brother would notice if it went missing and the family business would be ruined. He could try to win it back, but his luck at the racing track did not come in. As he could not make his own luck, he would make his own money.

He bought paper and ink and set to work. Feinstein had not noticed the forged bills. The plan worked until he tried to pay Dupe at the gaming house. Dupe would not be duped. Hart hoped he could bank on his brother's help. Not wanting to tell him about his debt, he staged a kidnapping and sent the ransom note to his brother - £1,000 genuine notes to be swapped for his home-made notes. But Ronald could not do it. It was his father's bank. If he took money from it, he would be ruined. He waited for more proof, and grisly proof he got.

To compel his brother to exchange the notes, Reggie cut off his own finger with the paper guillotine, making sure to leave his ring on to prove it was him. Knowing something as gruesome as this would pique my interest, he left it at my door. He hoped that Ronald's fear that my high profile would lead to a scandal would compel his brother to swap the banknotes more quickly.

Instead, his exile is likely to be transformed into imprisonment, the sentence for forgery being very steep indeed. But as Kenneth Dupe says, "You roll the dice, you pay the price".

Dear Reader,

Well done!

With your keen eye for detail and powers of deduction, you have solved these most intriguing cases. The fate of those responsible is being weighed by the scales of justice.

You have reunited a most beloved dog with its owner and sent those responsible to Scotland Yard. You helped to uncover a plot to steal a masterpiece and at the same time shone a light on a most talented copyist. You most certainly saved the life of a talented apprentice and uncovered a money laundering fraud whilst seeking out the owner of a severed finger.

It is of great assurance for me to know, should I have need, a fellow mind capable of solving the seemingly unsolvable is available to assist in bringing comfort to the poor souls who seek it at my door.

I can only hope, once word reaches the press, that villains intent on committing heinous acts against others take heed and reconsider. However, if my experience as the world's most famous detective has taught me anything, it is that while there exists a cloak of darkness, there will be those intent on concealing their true nature among its inky folds.

Until next time, reader.

Yours faithfully,

Sherlock Holmes